COLOR MY WORLD

Beautiful Nature

Illustrated by David Coviello

Great Barrier Reef – Queensland, Australia

At 14,429 miles long, the Great Barrier Reef is equivalent in size to 70 million football fields and can be seen from outer space.

As you color, look for these things:

O Clownfish (2)   O Submarine

O Crab (1)   O Sunken ship

O Daisies (3)   O Starfish (3)

O Scuba diver   O Treasure chest

Grand Canyon - Arizona, United States

Reaching up to one mile in depth and 18 miles across, the Grand Canyon is an impressive sight, but it is not the deepest or widest canyon in the world. The deepest canyon is the Cotahuasi Canyon in Peru, while the widest is the Yarlung Tsangpo Canyon in Tibet.

As you color, look for these things:

O Climbers (5)   O Hot-air balloon

O Hawks (3)   O Rafters (3)

Redwood Forest - California, United States

Redwoods are prehistoric trees, existing during the time of the dinosaurs. They can grow over 300 feet high and live for an average of 2,000 years.	As you color, look for these things:
	O Bird O Pinecones (2)
	O Dragonfly

Mount Fuji - Japan

Mount Fuji grew into one pristine peak from a collection of
smaller volcanoes in the area. The last time Mount Fuji erupted
was December 16, 1707, and it lasted until January 1, 1708.
The eruption was so powerful that temples as far away as
6 miles were destroyed, and ash was deposited 82 miles
away in the present-day Tokyo area.

As you color, look for these things:

O Baseball   O Cranes (3)

O Baseball bat   O Jet planes (3)

Mount Kilimanjaro - Tanzania

Mount Kilimanjaro is the tallest mountain not a part of
a mountain range, as well as the tallest mountain in Africa.

As you color, look for these things:

○ Bird

○ Flowers (3)

○ Elephants (2)

○ Snakes (2)

Lake Louise - Alberta, Canada

This glacial lake gets its emerald green hue from the finely ground particles of rock, often called rock flour, that get carried through the water as the surrounding glaciers melt.

As you color, look for these things:

O Canoes (3)

O Eagles (3)

O Loose teeth (2)

O Opossum

O Pontoon planes (2)

Dragon's Blood Trees - Socotra, Yemen

These trees are native to the island of Socotra, which is on the northern tip of Africa. They get their name from the deep red sap that seeps from their bark when pierced, and are often found growing from limestone-based soil.

As you color, look for these things:

O Birds (7)   O iPhone

O Flowering cactus   O Scorpion

Ashikaga Flower Park - Japan

The Ashikaga Flower Park is known for its many wisteria flowers, locally known as fuji. Its most popular attraction is the wisteria tunnel, a grassy 262-foot tunnel decorated with blue, purple, and yellow wisterias hanging from above. It is one of two such tunnels in Japan.

As you color, look for these things:

O Butterflies (2)   O Lightbulb

O Crane   O Shovel

O Ducks (3)

Llangernyw Yew - Wales

A legend says this tree is inhabited by a spirit called Angelystor, which in Welsh means "Evangelist" or "Recording Angel." Every Halloween night, a loud voice will announce the names of the townspeople who will die the next year. As the legend goes, a local man challenged the myth, only to hear his name called out by the tree spirit. The man then passed away within the next year.

As you color, look for these things:

O Ant hill

O Beehive

O Bottle

O Spiderweb

Monument Valley - Arizona and Utah, United States

This valley has been used as a filming location as far back as the late 1930s, including *2001: A Space Odyssey, Back to the Future Part III*, and *Forrest Gump.*

As you color, look for these things:

O Chopsticks

O Ice-cream sundae

O Scorpions (2)

O Stapler

O Sword

O Vultures (3)

Bamboo Gardens - Arashiyama, Japan

These gardens outside of Kyoto have been very popular since the late 8th century, usually with royals and high society. The bamboo of the groves, while visually pleasing, have also been used to make baskets, floor mats, and other goods for just as long.

As you color, look for these things:

O iPod

O Lipstick

O Scissors

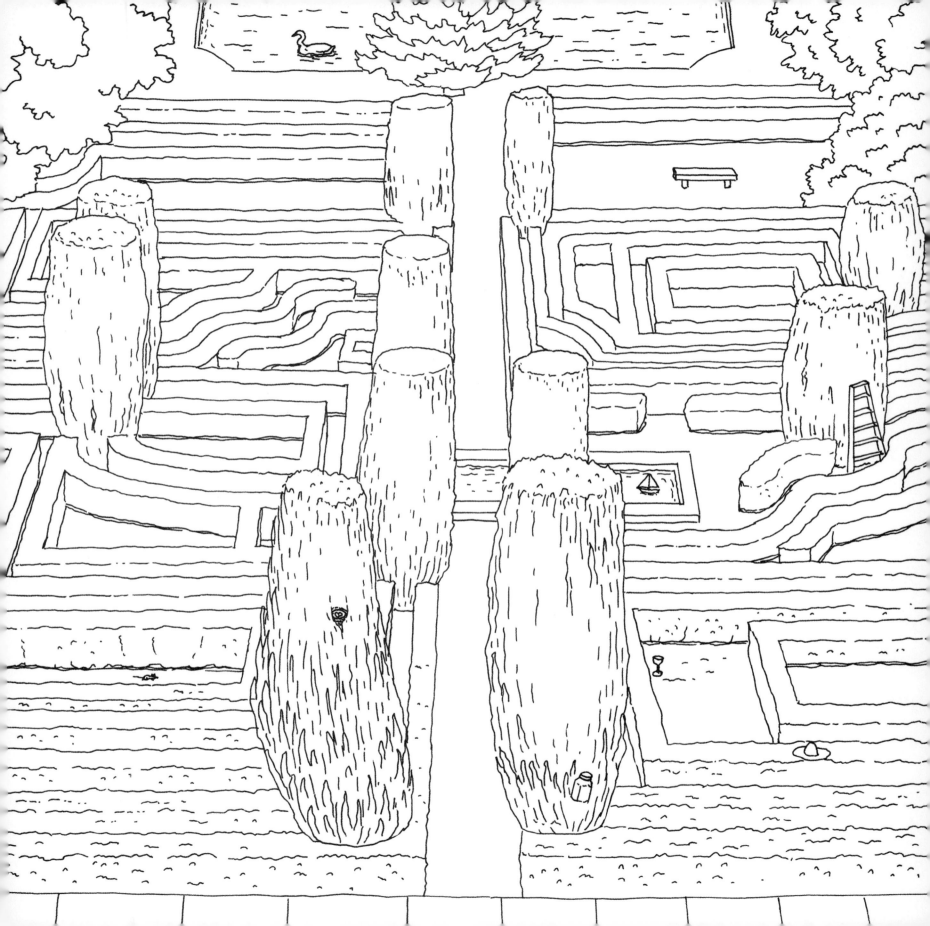

Sabatini Gardens - Madrid, Spain

Part of the Royal Palace, these gardens began construction in 1933. They were not complete until the 1970s, and opened to the public in 1978 by King Juan Carlos I. The gardens were named after Spanish architect Francesco Sabatini, who contributed to the design of the palace, but not the gardens.

As you color, look for these things:

O Birds' nest   O Mouse

O Hat   O Sailboat

O Ladder   O Swan

O Mason jar   O Wineglass

Bahá'í Gardens - Haifa, Israel

The most famous of the Bahá'í Gardens are the Terraces, also known as the Hanging Gardens of Haifa. Made up of 19 different terraces on the side of Mount Carmel, the path leads up to the Shrine of the Báb, the resting place for the founder of the Babi Faith. All of the gardens in Haifa are important holy places.

As you color, look for these things:

○ Cigar

○ Open book

○ Loaf of bread

○ Sunbather

Victoria Falls - Zambia

Due to the spray from the falls, the River Zambezi Rain Forest is the only place in the world that receives rainfall 365 days a year.

As you color, look for these things:

O Hot-air balloons (3)   O Lollipop

O Flamingo   O Ultralights (3)

Umshiang Double Decker Root Bridge - India

Even with the technique having been perfected by the
Khasis people of India, it still takes 10 to 15 years to
grow a root bridge. The good news is they last for about
500 years! This bridge in particular is the only double root
bridge in the world.

As you color, look for these things:

O Briefcase   O Snake

O Laptop   O Turtle

Earth Goddess - Atlanta, Georgia, United States

The Earth Goddess, now a permanent fixture in Atlanta's Botanical Garden's display, stands at 25 feet tall and is comprised of over 18,000 annual plants.

As you color, look for these things:

O Birds' nest   O Flowers (3)

O Bottle   O RC motorboat

O Broom   O Rubber ducky

O Coins (3)

Rice Terrace Fields - Mu Cang Chai, Vietnam

The 463 square miles of rice terraces were created in the 1400s by the Hmong people, by using a series of channels, natural waterfalls, and rivers to fill each one. During the rice-growing season of February to April, each terrace is filled with water, causing the entire area to act as one giant mirror of the sky.

As you color, look for these things:

O Dogs (3)   O Shark fin

O Ladder   O Umbrella

O Rice harvester

Carved Caves - New Mexico, United States

So far, it's taken American artist Robert "Ra" Paulette 25 years to carve intricate patterns and designs of everything from trees to hearts to flowers onto the walls. His intent is to inspire "spiritual renewal and personal well-being" for all who visit. Some people have even bought a few of his carved caves, though Paulette sees none of the profits. He does it for no other reason than personal enjoyment.

As you color, look for these things:

O Camera
O Millipedes (3)
O Candle
O Mouse
O Feather

The Wave - Paria Canyon, Arizona, United States

Created by millions of years of wind and water erosion, the multicolored rock formations are quite beautiful, but they're also very fragile. To keep traffic and damage to the area to a minimum, hikers and photographers who wish to visit have to apply for a lottery that dispenses only 20 travel permits per day.

As you color, look for these things:

O Beach ball   O Rope

O Cactus   O Vinyl record

Sandstone Pillars - China

These sandstone columns in Zhangjiajie National Forest Park were an inspiration for the landscape in the film *Avatar*. One of the larger columns was later renamed "Avatar Hallelujah Mountain."

As you color, look for these things:

O Eagle   O Rock climbers (2)

O Iced coffee   O Wind turbine

Lake Nakuru - Kenya

Though the name "Nakuru" translates to 'a dusty place,' the lake is home to many types of fish and water-adapted animals such as otters and hippopotamuses. One of its most striking features is over 1 million pink flamingos living there among 400 other species of birds and wildlife.

As you color, look for these things:

O Bottle

O Crocodiles (2)

O Elephants (2)

O Fisherman

O Vultures (3)

Seljalandsfoss Waterfall - Iceland

This nearly 200-foot waterfall is located just off Iceland's Ring Road, the route that connects travelers to many of the country's most stunning sights. Seljalandsfoss is one of the most well-known falls, since visitors can go behind the falls to a cave to watch the sunset.

As you color, look for these things:

O Basketball   O Flowers (3)

O Beehive   O Viking sword

Lauterbrunnen Valley - Switzerland

There are 72 waterfalls in this valley, so it's easy to understand why the name translates to "many fountains." The most famous of the falls, the Staubbach, is the inspiration for the poem *Spirit Song Over the Waters* by Johann Wolfgang von Goethe.

As you color, look for these things:

O Glider

O Parachuters (2)

O Solar panels (2)

O Wind turbine

Plitvice Lakes - Croatia

The Plitvice Lakes consist of a series of 16 lakes and waterfalls that tumble into each other. It is nearly impossible to study one lake individually, since the water from the many rivers that create the lakes constantly erode and change the landscape over a short amount of time. As one waterfall dries up, another is formed, constantly changing the depth, shape, and size of the lakes.

As you color, look for these things:

O Bottle   O Straw

O Hummingbird   O Rubber ducky

O Pencil   O Ruler

Punalu'u Beach - Maui, Hawaii, United States

Also known as Black Sands Beach, it gets its color from the remains of cooled volcanic rock that have been broken into small pieces by the tides. Hawaii has white, black, and even green beaches all over the islands.

As you color, look for these things:

O Helicopter   O Sunbather

O Outrigger canoe   O Surfboard

O Submarine

Mount Bromo - Indonesia

Mount Bromo is an active volcano that has erupted at least four times since 2004. During the Hindu festival of Yadnya Kasada, the Tenggerese people of the area travel up the side of the mountain with fruit, flowers, and other goods to make offerings to the gods of the mountain. After tossing the offerings into the volcano's outer crater, some believe that recollecting them after the ceremony will bring good luck.

As you color, look for these things:

O Coffee mug   O Parrot

O Football

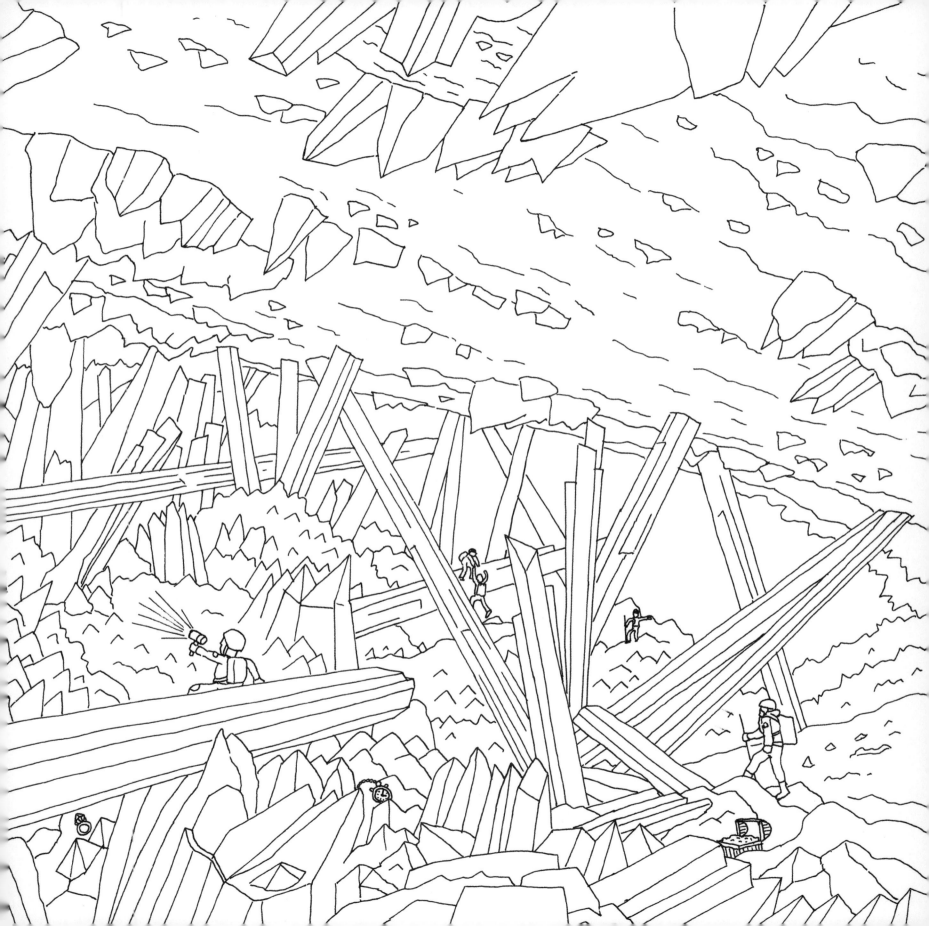

Cave of Crystals - Mexico

Discovered in 2000, the cave holds crystal pillars that are over a half a million years old. Many crystals are more than 30 feet long and weigh over 55 tons. Most of the cave has been unexplored due to the extreme conditions, with temperatures reaching 135°F along with 90% to 99% humidity.

As you color, look for these things:

O Diamond ring   O Treasure chest

O Pocket watch

Stone Forest - China

Covering a little over 193 square miles, the area was a large sea approximately 270 million years ago. The water slowly drained away, exposing the limestone bed to wind and water erosion. The impressive view has an old saying attached to it from the capital of the province, Kunming, which is: "If you have visited Kunming without seeing the Stone Forest, you have wasted your time."

As you color, look for these things:

O Boot

O Sock

O Pen

O T-shirt

Marble Caves - Chile

Located in General Carrera Lake, the second largest lake in Chile's Patagonia region, this network of caves is also called the Marble Cathedral because of its many high arches and the beauty of the turquoise waters' striking reflections.

As you color, look for these things:

O Baseball cap

O Crab

O Millipede

O Shark fin

Thor's Well - Oregon, United States

Approximated at around 20 feet deep, Thor's Well is a natural hole found off the coast of Cape Perpetua that continuously fills and empties with seawater. Though it is reportedly most striking when dramatic water gushes an hour before and after high tide, Thor's Well is incredibly unpredictable and dangerous. Due to the force of the waves ebbing and flowing, no one has explored the bottom.

As you color, look for these things:

O Bottle   O Dollar bill

O Crab   O Fish

Avenue of Baobabs - Madagascar

These specific types of baobab trees, known as Grandidier's baobabs, are the largest found in Madagascar, reaching close to 100 feet high. The trees used to be found clustered in thick forests, but are now more common to flat, wide-open areas.

As you color, look for these things:

O Bottle

O Candy cane

O Vase

O Warthog

Devil's Tower - Wyoming, United States

This rock formation was the first United States National Monument, instituted on September 24, 1906, by President Roosevelt. It is known to many Native Americans as a sacred site with names such as "Bear House" or "Bear's Lair." But due to a translator misinterpreting the name in 1875 as "Bad God's Tower," it was given the name "Devil's Tower." Many indigenous groups have attempted to have the name changed, but those requests have been denied.

As you color, look for these things:

O Buffalo (3)   O Candy corn (3)

Crooked Forest - Poland

Every tree in this forest bends at its base at a nearly 90-degree angle facing north. No one is quite sure why, but some believe the curves were man-made to create the hulls of ships. Others think it may have been the result of heavy snowfalls.

As you color, look for these things:

O Mouse   O Squirrel

O Owl   O Watch

O Rabbit

American Samoa

American Samoa—Samoa translates to "sacred earth"—is made up of a network of five volcanic islands and two coral atolls, and covers an area of about 76 square miles (a little larger than Washington, D.C.). There are only three native mammals that live there, all of which are a type of bat. The rest are either tropical fish or fowl.

As you color, look for these things:

O Aircraft carrier   O Canoe

O Bananas   O Drone

O Catamaran   O Sailboat

Jellyfish Lake - Palau

While this lake is composed of saltwater and does connect to the ocean, it is not affected by ecological changes that surround it. Because of this, the jellyfish in the lake have lost their ability to sting, and are safe to swim with.

As you color, look for these things:

O Boat

O Fish

O Oar

O Periscope

O Propeller beanie cap

Old Man of Hoy - Scotland

This sea stack of red sandstone eroded naturally into its shape by wind, water, and time, and is believed to be between 250 to 400 years old. As it continues to erode, small cracks are appearing all over the structure, and officials say it may soon collapse.

As you color, look for these things:

O Bagpipes

O Kayaks (2)

O Birds' nests (3)

Sonora Desert – Arizona, United States

The hottest desert in North America, the Sonora Desert is a 100,000-square-mile region that covers parts of Arizona, California, and Mexico. Certain areas see less than 3 inches of rain a year, with others seeing no rainfall at all. Summer temperatures easily reach 118°F. Despite this, the desert has a wide range of vegetation, from plains to even a tropical forest.

As you color, look for these things:

O Bees (2)   O UFO

O Bird

Hamilton Pool - Texas, United States

Located about 23 miles west of Austin, this pool is a popular spot for tourists and swimmers alike, and was purportedly discovered in the 1880s by an 8 year old. The pool is believed to have been created over thousands of years of erosion and exposed once the grotto that contained it eventually collapsed. There are also cultural remains around the pool that date back 8,000 years.

As you color, look for these things:

O Rattlesnake   O Teapot

O Spider   O Tourists (3)

Tunnel of Love - Ukraine

Because of the location of the train route in relation to its forest surroundings, the trees and other fauna have naturally molded around the shape of the locomotive. The local legend surrounding this tunnel says that if a couple is truly in love, and they complete the 2 mile walk together, they will be granted one wish that is bound to come true.

As you color, look for these things:

O Cup   O Hearts (3)

O Flower

Mendenhall Ice Caves - Alaska, United States

Located 12 miles south of Juneau, these caves are located inside a 12-mile-long glacier that is melting faster than before. It receded a half mile from 1500 to 1958, but since then has receded 2 miles. The caves are a result of this melting, and glow an ethereal blue due to the way the ice absorbs and reflects light from the outside.

As you color, look for these things:

O Baseball cap   O Pickax

O Coins (3)

Black Forest - Germany

The Black Forest got its name from being so thick in parts that no sunlight can hit the forest floor. The nearby spa town of Baden-Baden was a popular vacation spot for high society, with visitors ranging from Queen Victoria to Mark Twain to the family of Napoleon Bonaparte.

As you color, look for these things:

O Bird   O Trumpet

O Eyeglasses   O Sausage links

O Moth

The Dark Hedges - Northern Ireland

Planted in the 1700s, these trees were meant to impress guests on their way to the mansion of a wealthy family. Now, the area has been used as a filming location for the television show *Game of Thrones*.

As you color, look for these things:

O Ax

O Owl

O Pint of beer

O Rabbit

O Tire swing

Rainbow Bridge - Watkins Glen, New York, United States

The Rainbow Bridge is considered one of the most attractive parts of the park. Visitors can walk behind a waterfall, and once they reach the bridge, have a view of several pools and falls from above. The entire visit takes only about half a day.

As you color, look for these things:

O Desk lamp   O Playing card

O Life preserver

Yosemite Valley - California, United States

When Yosemite National Park was established in 1890, it did not include Yosemite Valley and its distinctive landmarks such as El Capitan and the Half Dome. Because these areas were not protected, miners, loggers, herders, and other laborers damaged the land. It wasn't until 1903 when President Roosevelt camped there that he decided it should also see conservation efforts. Three years later, Roosevelt signed into law the acts that put the valley under federal jurisdiction.

As you color, look for these things:

O Arrowhead　　O Forest fire

O Blimp　　O Teacup

O Hawk

Jigokudani Monkey Park - Japan

Despite having an elevation of 2,789 feet and experiencing snowfall for a third of the year, the name translates to "Hell's Valley" because of the steam and boiling water that seep from cracks in the frozen ground. Japanese macaques, or snow monkeys, flock to the hot springs most often during the winter, but appear year-round due to park attendants constantly feeding them.

As you color, look for these things:

O Ancient scroll   O Snowshoes

O Bananas

Fairy Pools - Island of Skye, Scotland

The water of the pools is crystal clear with tints of green and turquoise. It's suggested that because the colors of the water hint at an unnatural origin, that is the reason why they're called fairy pools, but no one is quite certain. Regardless of the name and their consistently frigid temperatures, they are very popular among swimmers.

As you color, look for these things:

O Barrel   O Turtle

O Dragonfly   O Swimmers (2)

Fjaðrárgljúfur Canyon - Iceland

This valley is 328 feet deep and a little over a mile long. The river that carved out this canyon over 9,000 years ago is not as deep and can be crossed easily with a sturdy pair of boots. The best time to visit is during the summer, despite there still being snow on the ground.

As you color, look for these things:

O Feather   O Kites (2)

O Flags (2)   O Tent

Roughting Linn Waterfall - England

Near these cascading falls is an outcropping of rock art that has hundreds of different carvings. There is no information detailing what they are or where they originated, but scientists believe they originate from prehistoric times.

As you color, look for these things:

O Bird   O Straw hat

O Inchworm   O Turtle

Angel Falls - Venezuela

At 3,212 feet tall, Angel Falls is the highest uninterrupted waterfall in the world. The falls evaporate during the warmer months, turning the water into mist before it even hits the ground. If there is a strong wind present, the mist can be felt a mile away.

As you color, look for these things:

O Maracas (2)　　　　O Tennis racket

O Salt and pepper shakers

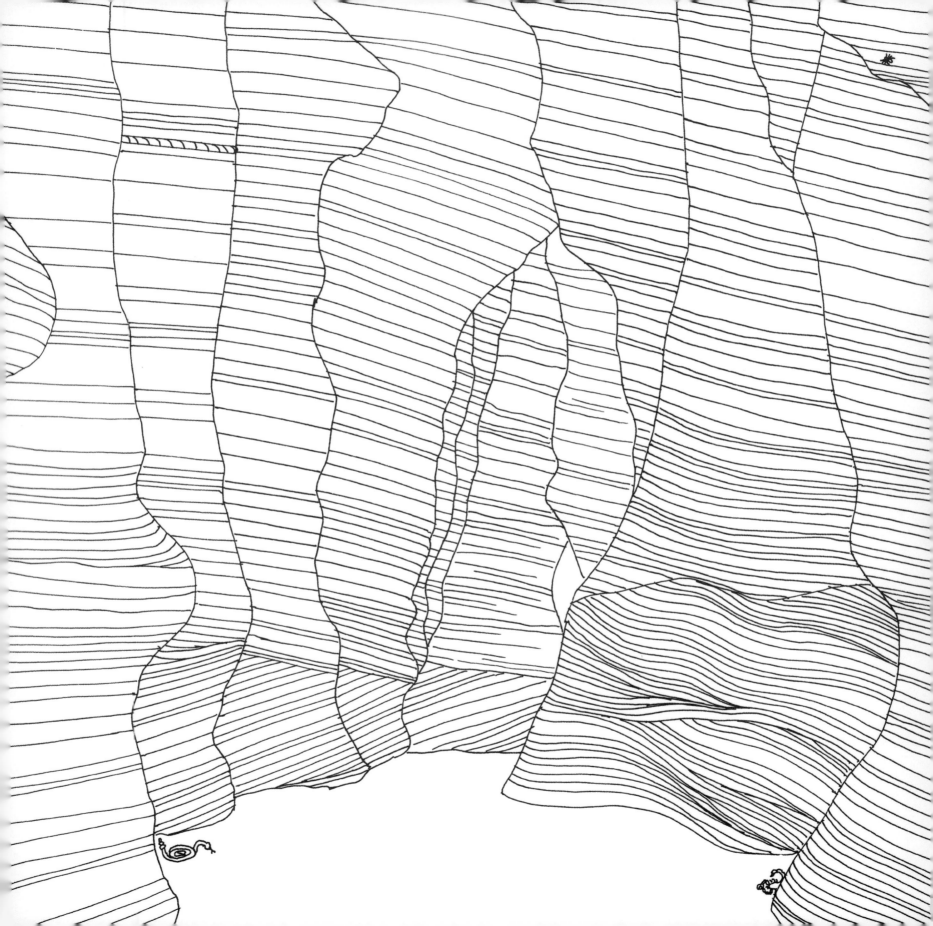

Antelope Canyon – Arizona, United States

Located in the center of the Navajo nation, Antelope Canyon is one of the most photographed canyons in the world, made famous by its naturally winding architecture and beams of light that stream inside. Even though there can be no direct rainfall, flash floods can still occur from rainfall further upstream. Ladders and other precautions such as a flash flood siren have been put in place for visitors' safety.

As you color, look for these things:

O Rattlesnake   O Scorpion

O Rope   O Spider

Tulip Fields - Holland

Tulips are extremely popular in Holland, and so valuable in the 1600s that they were used as currency. Today they are as synonymous with Holland as windmills. Many tulip fields are privately owned and not open to the public. However, there is a large garden called Keukenhof that is open to the public. It spans over 79 acres and is home to over 7 million hyacinths, daffodils and, of course, tulips.

As you color, look for these things:

O Barge

O Herd of cattle

O Pickup truck

O Windmill

Ngorongoro Crater - Tanzania

This crater is known as a caldera, the result of a massive volcano collapsing on itself after a large explosion. It's believed that before it collapsed, the volcano was as tall or taller than Mount Kilimanjaro (19,341 feet).

As you color, look for these things:

O Bunch of balloons   O Mushroom

O "Keep Off Grass" sign   O Table

Rakotz Bridge - Germany

Known as the Devil's Bridge, it was built in the 1860s with such precision and accuracy that, no matter from which angle it is viewed, its reflection makes a perfect circle. Crossing the bridge is prohibited in order to keep it intact.

As you color, look for these things:

O Candle   O Turtles (2)

O Dog   O Water snake

O Dragonfly

Glacier National Park - Montana, United States

This rich ecosystem that spans over 1 million acres with more than 130 named lakes, 1,000 types of flowers, and hundreds of different animals is often called the "Crown of the Continent Ecosystem" for its beauty and diversity.	As you color, look for these things: O Axe O Wolf O Bear

Serengeti National Park - Kenya and Tanzania

The Serengeti is over 12,000 square miles, so its name translates to "endless plains." It is also the largest and oldest ecosystem in the world.	As you color, look for these things: O Bowl O Helicopter O Crocodile O Snake O Elephants (2) O Teacup O Flamingos (3)

Green Lake - Austria

This park floods every spring when the snow from the Hochschwab mountains melts. The lake's water levels rise rapidly from 7 to 40 feet, and from 21,500 to over 43,000 square feet. The flooding lasts for only 3 to 4 months and is a popular time for snorkelers and photographers.

As you color, look for these things:

O Barrel

O Bobber with hook

O Canoe

O Fish (3)

O Hermit crab

O Message in a bottle

Padley Gorge Trail - Derbyshire, England

This path is one of the best ways to surround yourself in nature. All along this trail, remnants of a time long past can be found, like an old house used to store ice built into the hills, and large stone wheels discarded at the bottom of the gorge.

As you color, look for these things:

O Beehive   O Pitchfork

O Crown   O Tire swing

Hills of Tuscany - Italy

Among the beauty of these rolling hills, Tuscany and its capital city of Florence were the birthplace of the Italian Renaissance in the 1300s.

As you color, look for these things:

○ Bottle of olive oil ○ Roman column

○ Pitcher

Haiku Stairs - Oahu, Hawaii, United States

This trail, called the "Stairway to Heaven," reaches heights of over 2,500 feet, which is high enough to rise above clouds. It was closed to the public in 1987 due to liability concerns.

As you color, look for these things:

O Eyeglasses   O Tie

O Hot-air balloons (3)   O Wineglass

Salar de Uyuni - Bolivia

Spanning 4,086 square miles, 32 feet deep at the center, and containing approximately 10 billion tons of salt, Salar de Uyuni is the largest salt flat in the world. It's what's left of an enormous dried salt lake. When the bed floods during the wet season, the salt bed is covered in a thin layer of water, which results in a striking mirror image of the sky reflected on land.

As you color, look for these things:

O Bird   O SUVs (3)

O Coins (3)   O Tents (2)

Cliffs of Moher - Ireland

Reaching heights of up to 702 feet, these cliffs are not only one of the most popular tourist destinations, but also one of the most popular filming locations. These cliffs have been featured in movies such as *The Princess Bride* and *Harry Potter and the Half Blood Prince*, as well as various TV shows and music videos.

As you color, look for these things:

O Coonskin hat   O Seagulls (2)

O Rabbit   O Shamrocks (3)

Dolomites - Italy

This mountain range located in the northeastern region of Italy is protected by several national parks. During World War I, the line between the Austro-Hungarian and Italian armies ran through here. There are two museums on the mountain range dedicated to the range's importance in the conflict.

As you color, look for these things:

O Cheese wedge   O Gelato bowl

O Church   O Spoon

O Dairy cows (5)

Phi Phi Islands - Thailand

There are 6 islands that make up the whole of Phi Phi, which is derived from its original name of Pulau Api-Api, meaning "The Fiery Isle." Archaeological studies show evidence of the area being inhabited since prehistoric times.

As you color, look for these things:

O Boats (7)   O Flag of Thailand (3)

O Chili peppers (3)